DISCOVER BABY ANIMALS

Penguin

Written by Jennifer Boudart

Illustrated by Lori Nelson Field

Louis Weber, C.E.O.
Publications International, Ltd.
7373 North Cicero Avenue
Lincolnwood, Illinois 60712

www.pubint.com

Manufactured in China.

8 7 6 5 4 3 2 1

ISBN: 0-7853-7845-6

Ark! Ark! At the frozen seaside, the penguins greet each other with a loud barking noise. Father Penguin returns from a swim in the sea. It is now his turn to stay close to the nest so Mother Penguin can go fishing.

Mother Penguin climbs from the nest. Her movements wake her baby. Baby Penguin blinks her bright black eyes.

🐾🐾 FUN FACT

To leave the water, a penguin builds up its speed until it can leap, or "fly," out of the water and land on its belly or feet.

Baby Penguin is a bit of a slowpoke. When she was born, she took half a day to break out of her shell. It takes a long time for her to eat, too. And even though she is three weeks old, she has never left her nest.

Baby Penguin looks around. Penguins are everywhere, and they are all squawking loudly! They sure are noisy.

How do penguins keep their eggs warm?
The father penguin holds his egg on top of his feet so that it does not touch the ice. A flap of warm belly skin covers the egg and keeps it warm. Sometimes, the father has to do this for as long as two months while the mother is at sea catching fish.

Each family of penguins guards its nest. If a stranger gets too close, Father Penguin stretches his neck. His neck feathers fluff out. He points his head up to the sky and grunts. Baby Penguin stretches her neck and grunts, too.

Father Penguin and his baby tell the stranger to keep away from their home.

Can penguins fly?
Penguins are birds, but they cannot fly because their wings are too small to support the weight of their bodies. Penguins' wings are really more like flippers. These flippers are perfect for "flying" underwater.

Mother and Father Penguin must go fishing often to catch enough food for their tiny baby. They will have to leave her for a while. Baby Penguin's mother and father bring her to a group of young penguins. She slowly waddles after them.

Baby Penguin will be safe in this group. The older penguins will watch for danger.

🐾🐾 FUN FACT

Penguin parents put all of their babies in the middle of an adult circle, or creche, to shelter them from cold winds and predators. If an enemy approaches their babies, the adult penguins will beat their wings and screech, scaring the enemy away.

Baby Penguin snuggles with the others. She falls asleep. Baby Penguin does not notice the group moving away from her. She wakes up and sees a bird diving at her!

Luckily, an older penguin is nearby. The big penguin runs toward Baby Penguin, waving his flippers and barking loudly. He scares the bird away!

How do penguins protect themselves if they can't fly?

Penguins are very fast swimmers in the water. Since most of their enemies live in the water, penguins will swim swiftly and then jump on the land to escape.